The Old Ladies
of Nazareth

The Old Ladies of Nazareth

NAIM ATTALLAH

QUARTET BOOKS

First published in 2004 by
Quartet Books Limited
A member of the Namara Group
27 Goodge Street
London WIT 2LD

A catalogue record for this book
is available from the British Library

ISBN 07043 71162

Typeset by Antony Gray
Printed and bound in Great Britain by
Creative Print and Design

Your children are not your children.
They are the sons and daughters of Life's
longing for itself.
They come through you but not from you,
And though they are with you yet they
belong not to you.

KAHLIL GIBRAN, *The Prophet*

Preface

I wrote this little book over a period of three days in mid August 2004. I never planned it; it simply happened. The night when the thought of doing it came to me was very hot and humid in London. I was sitting out on the balcony of our apartment in Mayfair, overlooking a delightful garden below, my memories going back to how as a child I had so often sat on another balcony in another city long ago.

Suddenly there entered my mind a tale that I felt had to be told. It is the story of two wonderful old ladies who lived in the Holy Land, in the small town of Nazareth. The whole of their lives was a constant struggle for survival, punctuated by periods of exceptional hardship. They fought on all fronts with immense courage and a remarkable resilience that supported them through to the end.

This modest attempt to chronicle their lives seemed the best tribute I could pay to their memory. I only hope they will forgive me if in any way I have failed to paint a truthful and precise canvas of their sad, enriching tale.

Naim Attallah

Once upon a time there lived in the biblical town of Nazareth two old ladies. One was called Wardeh, which means 'Rose' in Arabic, and the other was called Jamileh, which means 'Beautiful'. Wardeh was well built and stout, with a round pinkish face that had angelic qualities, while Jamileh was painfully thin and had a pronounced hunch to her back. Jamileh would in fact probably have been considered rather ugly by today's standards. The sisters lived in relative domestic harmony, though there were occasions when this harmony was disrupted and a short-lived tension set in. This was usually the result of some misunderstanding over the daily chores. Each had her household tasks organized precisely, but just occasionally an overlap of duties led to a breakdown in the routine that was integral to their lives.

The chicken pen had to be cleaned at the crack of dawn. The sisters invariably rose with the morning star and the hens were set loose to roam the little plot of land surrounding the two-roomed house that had been the scene of their childhood. The rooms of the house had very high ceilings. Despite the heat, which could be stifling in summer, the rooms enjoyed a natural circulation of air. A series of vents in the walls where they met the ceiling kept the interior at a cool and rather refreshing temperature. In the hot season it made a pleasant contrast to the inferno outside.

Above the smaller room there was a tiny attic where food provisions could be stored. These included sacks of grain and jars of olive oil and vinegar, the vinegar being home-made during the grape season. The only access to the attic was by means of a ramshackle old ladder, which Jamileh would climb with great difficulty. She was always unsure of her balance on account of her various infirmities. Usually she succeeded in the hazardous task without moaning or asking for help, but at least once a year she fell off the ladder when her concentration failed or her legs gave way beneath her.

Just as the sisters' day always began with the morning star, so it ended when the sun disappeared below the horizon. Dusk was the time when their activities came to a standstill. Now they could partake of nature's repose. The peace and quiet of evening brought a serenity to their lives. They sat in the garden where there were, amid the profusion, certain flowers that they tended with special care, for these provided a reliable part of their meagre income. Normally they sold them to a church near by, and the monks, who were always on the lookout for a bargain, could never outwit Jamileh when it came to agreeing a price. She knew the open-market value for her flowers and always stuck to her guns. On one occasion one of the monks suggested she should donate the flowers to the church as an act of contrition for her sins. Jamileh was outraged. How could the church, far richer than herself, whose servants lived a life of so much comfort compared to her own, demand such a sacrifice from a poor old woman? Jamileh was less religious than Wardeh and nobody could ever remember seeing her at prayer or engaged in any other demonstration of piety.

The fertile garden gave them their livelihood. Apart from the flowers, they grew a range of vegetables, including such staple crops as onions and garlic, and there were lettuces, runner beans and potatoes. They also had aubergines, and two lemon and three pomegranate trees that fruited each year. A heavenly aroma was spread by the evening breeze as the leaves of the plants in the small herb garden gently nodded and swayed.

Every evening the old ladies sat in the same position at the same hour, watching the last rays of the setting sun fade beyond the surrounding hills. And then more painful memories from their youth would begin to mingle with the tranquillity. Those had been the years of the First World War, which had engulfed the whole of the Middle East, including their beloved Nazareth, still under the yoke of the all-powerful Ottoman Empire. They remembered the Allies coming over the hills and down into the valley where Nazareth lies, in pursuit of the Turkish soldiers running for cover.

Amid the pandemonium that followed, the sisters had gone to the stores depot where the Turkish army kept its provisions to join in the looting and ransacking. They brought away sacks of grain on their backs and anything else they could lay their hands on that might aid their survival. They took away as much as they could before the Allies had a chance to secure the depot and restore order among a hungry, frustrated population that lacked both food and sanitation. Often in later years they used to reminisce about how they had found ways to cope in a harsh world without the support of a family. They had been able to feed themselves from their little garden and to rely on nature to keep them alive.

Many years before then, Wardeh had been married at the age of eighteen. It had been an arranged marriage. She was never given the chance to get to know or even meet her husband before the event. He was reputedly a handsome man with striking features, renowned in Nazareth for his courage in battle and the bravery he displayed when challenged by adversaries. His engagement in the tribal warfare that was common in those days gave rise to legends of how many he had slain in battle, usually single-handedly. He was a fine horseman and he excelled in the martial arts. As a man of great physical strength and imposing presence, he inspired fear in his enemies but was known to be magnanimous in victory. The manner of his death, only a few months after his marriage to Wardeh, remains a mystery. Wardeh always refused to talk about him or the circumstances of her loss. It was only known that he was still in his thirties at the time and that he left Wardeh pregnant. In the face of Wardeh's silence on the subject, no one could ever work out whether she had been happily married, or if indeed she could have known her husband for more than a few days.

Three months after the tragedy, Wardeh gave birth to a baby boy. Her in-laws tried at first to take the boy away from her, claiming that she did not have the means to support him. This no doubt was true enough, but she refused to hand him over. Instead she took him to a German school in Jerusalem, which also functioned as an orphanage, and they accepted him. She would visit her son at the school as often as she could, but he was effectively brought up as a German and had to endure the regimented discipline of an institution run in accordance with a spartan German regime.

When it came to the First World War, and Germany was in alliance with the Ottoman Empire, the Germans claimed him as one of their own. He was drafted into the German army and found himself in a battalion stationed in Turkey. He rose through the ranks and was seconded as aide-de-camp to a senior German staff officer. Towards the end of the war he was taken prisoner by the Allies and remained in captivity for six months till he made his escape. Soon afterwards he was reunited with his mother.

Wardeh's relationship with her son was never a happy one. The upbringing in the German orphanage had left an indelible mark on him. He had grown into an embittered man who rarely saw the positive side of life; who felt he had no roots and was never throughout his life able to accept the reality of his origins. He felt no real attachment to his place of birth, nor did he recognize any aspect of his family's historical heritage. Instead he chose total isolation from his own kin. Not that Wardeh and Jamileh had any family that they knew of, but there were his relations on his father's side. The only half-hearted attempt he made to establish contact with them was merely perfunctory and fizzled out in no time at all. He considered his status to be above theirs, and in his view it would have lowered his standards to be associated with them. He had become a respected bank official who took his job seriously. He could not afford to be seen with his cousins, who were by and large a motley collection of shopkeepers and arms smugglers.

Among these cousins there were the good, the bad and the inconsequential. Unfortunately the good were inclined to be boring, while the inconsequential did not matter. The bad, however, were much more interesting. They had engaging ways with them that helped to negate the more dubious aspects of their professions. They lived in the oldest quarter of town in very ancient and primitive houses that could be reached only through warrens of winding alleys and were extremely difficult to find. For those who existed on the fringes of legality, these bolt-holes made a convenient refuge, and in an emergency, if the pressure were on, a very practical way of escape.

Wardeh and Jamileh had a lot to talk about each evening, for Wardeh's son was married by now. Thereby hung the tale of what had been another great disruption to their lives; but for the moment all that needs to be known is that he had his own family to raise; he sent his mother and aunt money on a regular basis to make their existence more comfortable. This money was never spent. Instead it was placed in a tin box and buried underneath the chicken shed. In the minds of the old sisters it would have been tantamount to sacrilege to break into it. They continued to live as they were accustomed to do, their garden producing everything for their subsistence. The money was superfluous to their modest needs.

Every morning, while it was still dark, Jamileh would go by the light of the stars to collect the eggs laid by the hens and place them, still warm, in a basket so she could sell them in the marketplace at sunrise. There was jubilation if the eggs were plentiful but deep despondency if the hens had not been laying. Jamileh's mood then changed as she berated the birds for failing in their duty and letting her down. With hands raised in anger she would threaten them with withholding their food supply. The hens, well able to sense when her anger was getting the better of her, clucked and scuttled out of reach in a panic. Yet common sense always reasserted itself after a while. As Jamileh returned to her usual self, she would start to call to the hens in a language they understood and throw them handfuls of grain. The relationship between Jamileh and her hens was a contentious one, but basically it was about mutual survival. Each party understood how to accommodate the other. If the hens did not lay they could not be fed. Money they were prepared to use was in short supply. The old ladies needed every contribution that the animals and nature could provide.

Wardeh and Jamileh gratefully accepted their lives of hardship. This hardship may seem to have been partly self-imposed, but they refused to spend money that they had not earned. It was for this reason that the subsidy sent by Wardeh's son needed to be tucked away in the tin box underneath the chicken shed. The hoard literally became a nest egg against the day when they might no longer be able to work so hard any more and needed to draw on it to fend off starvation. Their philosophy of life was too exacting and narrow to allow any flexibility in adapting to altered circumstances. They were powerless to change their mode of existence. It would have been unthinkable from their shared perspective to indulge in some unfamiliar extravagance just because a bit of money happened to be available at one particular time.

Their difficult upbringing had moulded them in tough, uncompromising ways. It had been beset with stringent rules and dogmatic attitudes that saw no virtue in encouraging in them the concept of choice. The girls were never sent to school. From the most tender age they were expected to work and were never allowed to live their childhood in the way that should have been their birthright. Nor did they have a chance to communicate in any real sense with the outside world, which they were brought up to believe was full of wickedness. Consequently they could neither read nor write and had to struggle with their illiteracy for the rest of their lives.

In this way the sisters' world came to consist of what they saw with their own eyes and what they heard from the limited circle of people with whom they had contact. They could never divert their minds by reading a book or acquiring the extra knowledge that might have eased their relentless routine. Instead it was through nature that they sought the answer to every problem. They invoked nature to heal their wounds, to treat a passing illness or a heightened fever. They turned to nature to tell them the time of day by the position of the sun in the sky. They could even judge the hour of the night from the changing pattern of the stars and planets. With nightfall their two rooms fell into complete darkness; they were dimly lit by an oil lamp only at times of sheer necessity.

Their beds were two mattresses on the floor, neatly arranged on either side of the main room. The second room, apart from being used to store provisions, was also a cooking area. This room was Jamileh's little daytime retreat. Here she would rest when it became too hot to venture outside. Here, too, she would medicate herself. There were sores all over her body that she treated by cauterizing them with a hot iron. The stench of burning flesh became nauseating, but Jamileh bore the pain with clenched teeth and a steely determination that saved her from passing out. She would salve the wounds afterwards with a herbal concoction of her own. An hour or so later, once she had recovered from the trauma of this procedure, she would rise to carry on with some unfinished task. Jamileh's strength was legendary. It was amazing, considering the state of her health and the way her whole life was a battle against vicissitude, how she managed to live to such a great age.

At the far end of the garden was a lavatory. It was primitive even by oriental standards. To use it you had to crouch to relieve yourself, and you needed to bring a bucket of water with you to flush it clean. It was not an enviable experience to have to answer a call of nature in the middle of the night, especially during the rainy season. The old ladies did not even possess an umbrella to hold over their heads. They could only struggle through the dark, water container in hand, braving the wind and getting soaked to the skin. Returning to the house, they had to struggle to change out of their saturated clothes in the dark before they were able to settle down again to sleep.

When they first lay down in bed at night, they invariably began a conversation concerning their day's work, the chronic ailments that had come upon them with old age, their worries about the state of the garden, the lack of rain, the low water level in the well on which they relied to keep the garden irrigated, and many of the other topics that old people talk about. For old age was beginning to sap their energies. They were aware of becoming more vulnerable to disease, of being less able to cope with the wear and tear of time. Their nightly conversations would often be interrupted by the bell ringing from an adjoining convent that housed nuns belonging to a closed order. Behind its high walls, built to keep prying eyes away and protect them from any intruder, the nuns lived totally isolated from the outside world, their lives dedicated solely to the glorification of Christ.

The two old ladies found some comfort in considering the similarity between their own life and that of the nuns. They all toiled, but to a different purpose. The old ladies sought simply to survive, to continue to endure, with no guarantee of heavenly reward, whereas the nuns laboured in anticipation of a world beyond the present one. The old ladies had no choice but to resign themselves to a life of discomfort, while the nuns had become prisoners of holy poverty by choosing self-denial. There was somehow an irony in the comparison. In terrestrial terms, the nuns were perhaps far worse off than their elderly neighbours, for they had no freedom at all to do as they wished.

At least the old ladies enjoyed the blessed gift of independence and thought themselves fortunate to have attained it.

During the long watches of the night, one of the old ladies might lie awake as the other slept, and vice versa. In this way their thoughts and dreams continually intermingled with reality. If both found themselves wakeful, they would start to exchange tales of the old days, or tell each other their dreams, which were but a reflection of the present. Wardeh's mind was often on her son and how it had been after his return from the war. He was a complex character who viewed the world with a pessimism that apparently deprived him of any sense of joy or of having ambitions beyond those of finding a secure job to give him some status in society. Yet he was none the less sociable. People who knew him only on the outside often found him a most engaging individual and thought highly of him. Although his jovial moods were rare, when he was in one he could charm all those he met. Another aspect of his personality was an explosive temper that he could not control. It was a trait that would cost him dear in the years to come. His reunion with his mother after the war had been fraught with emotion; but with the passage of time the son could hardly bring himself to acknowledge his mother and her unmarried sister. At its best the relationship involved effort on both sides, below the surface of which the tension simmered.

Not long after he returned from Turkey, he found work in an Egyptian bank, which was later taken over by a British bank. He moved from the backwaters of Nazareth to the big city, and took his mother and aunt with him. The idea was that they would keep house for him and make his life comfortable. Yet the tension was always present, created by the deep gulf that lay between education and literacy and the lack of such advantages. Any tolerance that existed was artificial, and the signs of the situation bursting at the seams began to grow stronger. At the age of thirty, he had found himself a fiancée of seventeen. She was still at school and her father was a well-known tailor and cloth merchant who traded mainly with Egypt. In this future son-in-law he saw a suitor who had all the necessary qualities. Here was a young man who was serious in his attitudes, who never deviated from the conventions and customs of the time. He had a steady job with a monthly income and was being looked after by two conscientious, sensible relatives – his mother and aunt. These two would help him to provide an adequate, well-run home for his young bride. What more could a father hope for? He was happy to bestow his daughter's hand in marriage. The wedding took place and it was a memorable occasion.

The bride came from a very religious Catholic family who were strict and devout in observing the church's teachings. She had three sisters, one of whom was about to be canonized by the Pope as a saint. Her authenticated miracles were the talk of the town and the family was beside itself with joy that they would soon be able to count a saint among their number. The son's new wife moved into the top floor of the large house he inhabited with his mother and aunt, situated in what was then known as Mountain Road. The top storey of the house was spacious and self-contained and ideally suited to accommodating a young family. But despite this physical separation from Wardeh and Jamileh in their lower quarters, the rows soon began, and they were to continue for nearly fourteen years. To the outside world they seemed a united family, especially as the number of its children grew at a pace of three years between each birth: three girls and a boy. The eldest was a girl of thirteen when the crisis finally came to a head.

Calamity struck when Wardeh's son was in one of his darkest moods and went into a vicious, uncontrollable rage. He evicted his mother and aunt from the house with an ugly display of ferocity that was quite unnecessary, and literally threw them out on to the street. There had been a great commotion, with a fair amount of shoving and pushing, and whether or not the reality was as harsh as this description implies, the end result was far from pleasant. Wardeh and Jamileh were bruised in the struggle and found themselves homeless in the big city.

They first sought refuge at a Protestant church in the German quarter. Within the compound of the church there lived a blind upholsterer whom they had often visited over the years. They had formed a close bond with the blind man, and he welcomed them with open arms. He was ready to share his lodging and food with the two old ladies he had grown to like and respect.

At first the two sisters could not stop crying, and the physical hurt they had suffered was clear for all to see. For a time they were inconsolable. It was as if their whole world had collapsed about them and they could no longer see any point in continuing to live. The blind man, however, was philosophical in his perspective on this terrible incident, though deeply sympathetic to their sad predicament. Throughout the ordeal he cautioned them about the total disaster that faced them unless they could, so to speak, dust themselves off and muster every grain of strength to overcome the effects of the tragedy. They stayed with him for two weeks before going back to their old home.

The two-roomed house had been let during their years away in the big city. Returned to Nazareth, they welcomed the restoration of a routine that took them back to their roots. They rarely talked about the experience of their eviction. Time was for them the great healer. All could be forgiven and conveniently forgotten. The old ladies were selective enough in their wisdom to remember the good things that had happened and cast aside the consequences of human frailty. It was as if their personal existence counted for little, for they believed that ultimately the good must overcome the bad. In the meantime, reflection and tolerance would make the painful things bearable and less awful than they may have seemed at the time.

They never spoke ill of another soul. Only Jamileh had a bee in her bonnet about what she referred to as the 'greedy church'. She never minced her words on the subject. Her accusation was that the church took money from the poor and disadvantaged so that its monks and priests could drink wine to compensate for the trials of celibacy. Jamileh was a strong character who never flinched from expressing her views and never doubted that her observations were true. Her dogmatism had its downside, though, since it made her a natural target for those who would poke fun at her. She was easily provoked into sharp reactions by a teasing comment or a concealed challenge. Wardeh, on the other hand, took any ribbing or banter in her stride, never batting an eyelid. No amount of teasing could ruffle her equanimity.

There was a poor lunatic in the neighbourhood who was constantly pursued by the catcalls of young boys as he walked the streets. He would never react until they started whistling at him, which always set him off into a rage. He then began to hurl stones in retaliation. Great were the disturbances that followed him all along his route. Once Wardeh asked him why he reacted so violently on hearing someone whistle; perhaps the whistling was not meant for him. He was not so mad, he retorted, that he could not recognize his own whistle.

The sisters' domestic circumstances may have lacked the comfort and security they had enjoyed while sharing the house in the big city, but it was less strenuous emotionally to be away from

Wardeh's son's growing family. They were content to re-embrace the natural rhythms of their garden and the work it demanded from them. Its ever-changing patterns were easier to cope with than the constant need to guard against provoking irrational eruptions in human behaviour. On the other hand, they missed the children terribly. Above all they missed the boy, for although the three girls were as deeply loved, it was the boy's absence that caused them the greatest grief. They would willingly have sacrificed their lives for him. He became the apple of their eyes, their very *raison d'être*. Everywhere they looked in the garden they could see his image. Under the shade of the trees, in the moving clouds, in the darkness of the night, he was a spark of light for them. He was the son they wished they could have had. He was their hope for the future. Through him they could see the way to new horizons and calmer seas. He would be their ultimate salvation in a cruel and uncaring world.

Wardeh often pondered on the way the boy had suffered ill-health since early childhood. The local doctor was a regular visitor to the house in Mountain Road. The boy seemed to contract every possible ailment. Afterwards he had to spend a lot of time in bed until he recovered. His inability to fend off disease was a constant source of concern. The doctor diagnosed anaemia and prescribed raw liver and beetroot, along with an injection to be administered three times a week. After a severe attack of dysentery, the boy had to gulp down great quantities of steamed rice and lots of goat's yoghurt. When he developed an acute form of tonsillitis, Wardeh and Jamileh had sat at his bedside throughout the night, dabbing his forehead with a cold wet cloth to bring down the intensity of the fever. Worse was to come when he was diagnosed with pneumonia. How many times did Wardeh then go out on to the balcony above the street at night, her arms outstretched to the heavens as she pleaded with the Good Lord to spare the life of her grandson? The illness became so severe that in addition to following the doctor's professional advice they also resorted to a traditional oriental remedy. Hot cups were applied to his back to draw blood. The rims left scars as a permanent reminder of how serious his illness had been.

Wardeh would hardly have been able to survive herself if the boy had failed to recover from his bouts of illness. Jamileh, who was equally fond of him, reacted impassively, showing no outward sign of emotion. Although she never gave any clues as to whether she believed in the power of prayer, she always comforted Wardeh with reassurances that he would come through these alarming crises, for she could see he was a born fighter despite the frailty of his body.

In Nazareth the boy continued to be a topic of conversation for the old ladies, especially in the winter months, when the shutters were closed and the wind outside howled in competition with the ringing of the convent bell. The talk was not all gloomy. Sometimes they recalled one episode in particular that made them laugh. It had happened a few months before their eviction from the big city when, out of desperation, Wardeh's son was seeking the views of many old and wise people as to how best to deal with his son's persistent ailments. How, he wanted to know, could he somehow boost the boy's immune system? The suggestion was put forward that circumcision might help, though no one was able to give a single scientific reason why it should. But desperate people adopt desperate measures. It was decided that it could do no harm, and might even do some good, to circumcise the boy. Had circumcision not been practised by the Jews since time immemorial? Was it not part of the covenant with God described in the Old

Testament? The only question arising was who would be able to perform the act of circumcision? The doctors in that part of the world were not experienced enough to do the operation with confidence and were often reluctant to try. The only people with the knowledge and experience to carry it out were the rabbis, for whom it was a routine – almost daily – task.

Contact was made with an Orthodox rabbi, who came round to Mountain Road with his long knife without delay, but presented himself to start with at the wrong house. As he could not speak any language other than Hebrew, he kept showing the knife and muttering the word 'baby', frightening the life out of the neighbours before the situation could be explained to them. Wardeh was present in the room when the rabbi arrived and performed the little operation. The boy screamed piteously and Wardeh could not stop the tears running down her face at what she could only see as a ghastly ritual beyond her understanding. Ironically, however, the boy became stronger soon afterwards. Who could say whether this was a direct result of the circumcision, or simply a natural progression as his body developed the ability to fend off infection? Perhaps it was one of those fateful acts that determine the successive stages of our development. Whatever the reason, the boy was out of danger where his health was concerned and he could begin to look forward to a more normal and stable childhood.

Certainly his childhood became more normal, at least in the eyes of the outside world. Within his own home, however, his childhood continued to be an overprotected one. He was constantly under supervision lest he should fall or come in any other way to some physical harm. So much of his childhood seemed to be spent crouched on the balcony of the house in Mountain Road, looking down on the world below. He saw children of his own age playing in the street, having fun and skipping for joy as they went past. He felt like a prisoner in his own house, rarely allowed to take part in any activity that might have an element of danger. This obsessive avoidance of risk should have been too absurd to last long, yet his parents persisted in shielding him so zealously that the best part of his childhood passed him by. He was destined, even when he reached his early teens, to be unable to swim, cycle or pursue any sport with a sense of adequacy.

As the Second World War got into full swing,
Wardeh's son became very preoccupied with his
banking activities. He was in charge of paying the
Allied forces stationed in Palestine. The pressure he
was under made him more short-tempered than ever
before; the atmosphere in his home deteriorated
even further. He began to inspire greater fear than
that occasioned hitherto by his erratic behaviour.
He ran the household like an army barracks, with
himself as supreme commander.

His children avoided him as far as they could.
They were seldom to be seen in his presence. Their
apprehension always grew as the hour came closer
for his return from work in the late afternoon. There
was no knowing what mood he might be in. They
glued themselves to the windows so they could see
him when he began to negotiate Mountain Road
and then run to warn of his impending arrival. The
moment of his entrance would always be fraught
with drama. Every member of the family withdrew
to their rooms, except for his wife, who would be

[35]

laying the table for his late lunch. If the food displeased him, he would make a scene and demand an alternative which he knew was not readily available. It was extremely difficult to divine what he might like to eat on any one day in particular. Everything was dependent on his mood, and whether his appetite was more selective than usual and therefore harder to accommodate. He treated his wife with little consideration, and made it his purpose in their marriage to reduce her to a cipher who echoed his views. He showed her no appreciable kindness. Indeed, at times when his temper flared he harassed her physically and smashed any domestic crockery that came to hand. Whenever his temper consumed him he became a monstrous figure, yet in calmer moments he always regretted what he had done. He would cry like a child, ask for forgiveness and show exaggerated signs of physical affection. He became demonic when he lost control, but the moment his demons were in retreat you would never have guessed that such a side to his character existed.

Wardeh and Jamileh had learnt to their cost just how far this instability could go. They were always fearful of the effect his temper might be having on the family. 'It is the German discipline,' Jamileh would declare in their conversations, 'that's turned him into this freak person, who is so wrapped up in himself and has all these terrible bouts of temper. The schooling was too harsh in its methods,' she would continue. 'It has encouraged him to be as he is – a man with no control over his inner fires.'

During the Second World War the sympathies of Wardeh's son were firmly with Germany, even though he was relying on the Allies for his living. For the best part of the night he listened to the radio, tuning in to the broadcasts from various German stations. Since German was his natural language, he was able to follow the progress of the German army closely and he greeted any news of an Axis win in battle with intense delight. This was perfectly understandable, for he considered himself to be more German than anything else. The way the British Mandate was administered in the Holy Land had won few friends among the Arab population, who believed it to be biased in favour of establishing a Jewish home in Palestine. The Arab uprising against the British had been put on hold for the duration of the war, on the understanding given by the British Government that the issue of Palestine would be resolved once the war was over, with fair discussions held between all parties. Time would tell whether these promises would be fulfilled as specified.

Meanwhile the preoccupation of Wardeh's son with the war so engrossed him that for a while it seemed to neutralize his temper and tensions briefly subsided in the household. The radio became his window on world events. He was utterly riveted, day in, day out, as the latest news came across the airwaves. The newscasts were often interrupted by bursts of music. Occasionally Mozart would be played, but if there was to be a portentous announcement – as when Hitler was scheduled to address the German nation – then only the spirit of Wagner would do. The prospect of hearing the Führer himself always put Wardeh's son into a state of high excitement. Every station in occupied Europe would announce the impending broadcast, always preceded by at least two hours of classical music, drawn from a repertoire including Bach, Beethoven and the Strauss family but culminating inevitably with Wagner.

The boy was fascinated by the terrific build-up of atmosphere. Although he hung back in the shadows, he could sense the electricity in the air and felt he was about to be engulfed by something tremendous. Then, as the moment of Hitler's speech came close, the tension mounted yet further and chairs were arranged nearer to the radio. There was an invitation to the whole family to listen to the broadcast. They dutifully took their seats, though none except the father was able to understand a word of it. Nevertheless the power of Hitler's delivery came across with compelling effect.

The father was in his element as he translated every word of the speech into Arabic with total precision. The speech was highly repetitive at times, but Wardeh's son reproduced the extraordinarily hypnotic quality of the language that Hitler used to such advantage. Hitler's oratory may not have been particularly literate, nor did it have any philosophical depth, but no one could deny that it achieved its objective: capturing the hearts and minds of the German people. The boy, in his all-unknowing innocence, could not fail to be impressed.

As the tide of war turned and it became clear that Germany was facing defeat, Wardeh's son sank into an ever deeper depression. The dark moods returned. Once again it was his family that had to bear the brunt of them. It was not that he was drawn to fascism. He supported Hitler because he saw Germany as his adopted motherland and could speak the language fluently without a trace of accent. Like many other people at the time, he was totally unaware of the horrors being inflicted on the Jews and other minorities by the German regime in the territories it controlled. He was German in spirit and suffered from tunnel vision. He was incapable of accessing the reality of the situation.

Amid all this turmoil of suffering, he would often go to the Jewish quarter of the city, where the inhabitants were mainly German-speaking Jews. He would converse in German for hours with men who were highly qualified in their professional lives. Going about the German quarter, he would indulge his hobby of buying *objets d'art*: paintings, furniture and glass. He became an avid collector. One room in the house was turned into what was practically a museum; it was a room the children were never allowed to enter. The cherished objects it contained formed a collection to be shown off with pride to visitors. He constantly marvelled at the workmanship and artistry of all the pieces displayed on the walls and tables. Later he was drawn especially to antique carpets, which became his true passion.

The boy had absolutely nothing in common with his father, except for this one thing: a simple instinctive love of the arts. His grandmother and great-aunt were relieved to notice that he displayed no signs of the violently unpredictable mood swings that plagued his father and everyone around him. Instead the boy was showing a zest for life that was contagious, despite all the difficulties at home. He seemed to have inherited from his father only his more positive traits. In any case, every night as he lay in bed he consciously struggled with the thought that he must not grow up to be like his father. The struggle itself opened his eyes to the sort of pitfalls that were bound to lie ahead along life's rocky road.

As the Allied victory was confirmed in Europe, so local unrest over the founding of a Jewish state in Palestine began to simmer again. Both the Arabs and the Jews launched a guerrilla war against the British, though the hostility from the Arab side was more pronounced. As the Arab campaign grew in intensity, the Mountain Road area increasingly became a target for sniper fire and life was made very precarious.

The old ladies in Nazareth heard the news from the big city with apprehension. Their memories went back to an incident in the mid 1930s when the family was woken at five o'clock one morning and all of them, including the children, were bundled into trucks by British soldiers. They were allowed to take no proper clothing with them. The trucks transported them to a large stadium, there to spend the whole day without food or water. It was intended as a communal punishment in retaliation for some act perpetrated by a freedom fighter that had resulted in a British casualty. Those were days when the family had lived in fear, dreading the knock on the door which was likely to herald rough treatment at the hands of a bunch of thugs.

The boy had been five years old when all of that happened. Now he was fifteen, and his father decided he ought to be sent to Nazareth to be out of harm's way. The old ladies were ecstatic. For the past few years they had seen almost nothing of him. Now he would be coming to live with them and they could get to know him properly at close quarters. Their preparations began in earnest. A clean mattress was laid in the most desirable spot in the big room and made up with linen sheets.

For his part, the boy was just as excited. Besides living with his granny and great-aunt, he would get to sample a freedom he had never yet enjoyed. He was going to be able to do as he wished and start to discover the outside world without the constraints imposed on him at his family home. Arriving in the primitive environment where the old ladies lived, he at once found the discomfort more appealing than anything he knew in Mountain Road; the rugged nature of these new surroundings made a welcome change. There was no running water and the only drinkable source was the Fountain of Mary, half a mile away. Going to fetch the water, he observed the bedouin women also coming to the fountain with their large earthenware jars. They would fill these receptacles with the heavenly cool water and place them on their heads, with a cloth ring to steady them, before walking away with a balanced poise and grace that was a delight to watch. It had been one of Jamileh's daily tasks to fetch the drinking water, but the boy gladly took it over from her so he could feast his eyes on the young bedouin women. In the bright sunlight, their faces revealed a dark beauty untarnished by modern cosmetics. It was a beauty that was entirely natural, unadulterated. He had never seen anything to compare with it in the faces of women in the Westernized big city.

The boy's new home was very strange to him, yet refreshing. When he was there at first he missed the street lighting of the big city and was frightened of the dark, though he would never have admitted it. During the night, if he woke and felt the urge to go to the lavatory at the far end of the garden, fear gripped his heart. Then he would wake up his grandmother to get her to go with him under some pretext. Usually he said it was because he was afraid of stumbling in the dark as he was not familiar with the lie of the land. She always knew this was not the real reason, but without a murmur she would follow him. She sat herself on a large flat stone a few feet away and waited for him to finish. Every now and then he chatted away to her to make sure she had not gone away. The fear was short lived. Before long he would embrace the darkness and welcome it as a good companion, rejoicing in its peace and serenity.

Not long after his arrival in Nazareth the boy was struck down by a mystery illness that sapped his energy and made him delirious with fever. His whole body ached and during the night he started going into convulsions as the fever reached its peak. The old ladies became deeply concerned as they recollected the episodes back in the big city when every one of the boy's childhood illnesses had turned into a major crisis. A visibly agitated Wardeh prayed as was her invariable habit at moments of stress, but it seemed to her this time that the power of prayer might not be enough on its own.

They summoned a doctor, an Austrian largely engaged in charitable work with the poor in Nazareth, who suspected a strain of virus and felt the fever would probably subside in a few days. He recommended small doses of aspirin and plenty of liquid, but said if there was no improvement in that time, he would like to move the boy into the local hospital for observation. The boy panicked at the thought of hospital. He felt confident that he was going to get better and declared that, whatever happened, he did not want to be separated from the care of his grandmother and great-aunt.

As soon as they heard this, Jamileh took the initiative. She went off in search of an old witch who was reputed to practise occult medicine. The prolonged healing ceremonies she used involved the burning of incense and the invocation of mysterious powers. Jamileh tracked the old sorceress down in the lonely cave that she called home, and the witch duly made her rather bizarre appearance to do what she could for the boy. The witch was all that a witch should be: painfully ugly with demonic features. Her long bony hands were covered with dried blisters, probably left by severe burns.

However scary a sight the boy found the old crone, he was too ill to care by this time. Destiny would have to take its course. The witch began by smearing a warm mixture of mud and ash on his forehead, rubbing it in gently before turning away to chant and gyrate herself into a frenzy. She then rubbed his chest and back with a thick herbal cream and covered his entire body with a large linen cloth. This, she indicated, should remain in place for at least three hours. The ritual over, she was given a few eggs by Jamileh in appreciation for her services and departed in haste, highly delighted to have earned her supper. The most astonishing aspect of the whole event was that the boy awoke next day feeling much better; the day after that he was fully recovered. Whereas Wardeh attributed this sudden recovery to divine intervention, Jamileh was inclined to believe it was down to the sorceress and her magic spell.

The boy's grandmother and great-aunt continued to fuss about him all the time, but without encroaching on his privacy. They would tell him tales of bygone days when Nazareth was set in open fields, where shepherds wandered, tending their sheep. They would often take him to the souk to buy a special piece of meat or some olives. He went with them to the mill when they took their grain to be ground into flour. He watched the old men in the cafés, smoking their narghiles contemplatively. He relished every aspect of these novel experiences. At sunset he joined the old ladies for their evening chat, reviewing with them the events of the day. Even after they were all in bed, they went on talking and planning out the tasks they would do the next day. At the height of summer they slept with the shutters wide open and the breeze that circulated in the room brought with it the delicate aromas of the flowers in the garden. He was learning so much in such a short time and each day seemed the beginning of another adventure, bringing a new topic for conversation or a memory to be treasured.

The life of the old ladies, too, was one they now felt they were living to the full. There had been so many years of isolation for them, with nothing to look forward to. The arrival of Wardeh's grandson to live in their midst as a focus for their attention was a piece of unexpected good fortune they could never have dared hope for. The divide between old age and youth dissolved. They would talk on in the dark about the wonder of it till sleep overtook them.

Before it was even light in the morning the boy would be awake, hearing the sounds of Jamileh chasing her hens and Wardeh attending to her pigeons. The pigeons would be eager to fly from their roosts after a good night's rest. They would wheel into the air and disappear over the town, and not return till evening, when they were counted back one by one to make sure none had gone missing. The morning routine always included the barter of some fresh eggs for a basket of figs or two or three ladles of goat's yoghurt from a bedouin woman who often called by to see if there was anything they wanted. It was as if history had stood still and they were back in biblical times.

In the mornings the boy often roamed about the town before the sun got too hot. He began to track down his unknown relatives on his father's side. They all lived in Nazareth. The boy was anxious to uncover his roots. Unlike his father, he wanted to have a real sense of belonging. He became aware of a desperate hunger within himself to share a common heritage with others of his own blood. Then he would no longer be so alone, but would find those who would fend and fight for him, who could offer him support and comfort. He spoke about his feelings to his grandmother and great-aunt and both encouraged him to seek out his relatives if that was what he wanted. It was indeed: his mind went back to the endless hours spent on the balcony of the house in Mountain Road as a forlorn, miserable kid, seeing practically nothing except what happened in the street so far below and out of reach. He could no longer accept being caged, even if the cage were golden.

The old ladies gave him some directions and soon he made contact with his relations. For their part, they were delighted to meet him and fêted him for almost a week. He found himself whirled into a varied family group consisting of the young, the old and the infirm. One, who owned a grocery store and seemed to have standing as the most respected member of the clan, was the only cousin his father really acknowledged. He was charming and generous to the boy and paid him a lot of attention. The boy found himself being taken into the heart of the family he had never known and being showered with a love and affection he had not experienced until now. The boy started to adore the new life and was beginning to relish Nazareth. He began to make many friends of his own age and gained popularity in the neighbour-hood. The camaraderie he had yearned for, the companionship and the close relationships, were suddenly his for the taking.

There was another member of the family who began to exert a deep fascination. He was a man in his forties who was known as the black sheep. It was whispered that apart from making his living as a gun runner he was also a contract killer. The one certain thing was that the black sheep was feared by everyone in town. Under his white flowing robe he carried a gun wherever he went, and the scene as he walked along a street was like something out of a Western film. The crowds would part to give him a clear passage. He was invariably given the most prominent seat in the café he frequented, and he would sit there most of the day, smoking and receiving a continuous procession of people who all seemed to be reporting to him on some matter or other. The respect he commanded was probably inspired by fear. As he went about the town he was like a peacock patrolling its territory.

In return for the attention the boy was paying him, the black sheep showed him great warmth. There was a sense of safety in his company. It made the boy feel good. One day he invited the boy to come and have lunch with him at his house. This was tucked away in a warren of twisting alleys somewhere in the souk district. The black sheep's wife and thirteen-year-old daughter came to join the boy when lunch was served. They all ate sitting on the floor, supported by a comfortable set of cushions, as was still customary in those parts of town. Afterwards they retired to a small oriental sitting-room for Turkish coffee. It was apparent that the young girl was very much in her father's favour. She snuggled up to him during the first part of the boy's visit and it was clear their love was mutual. Abruptly, however, her father gestured to her with his hand. She stood up, said goodbye and left.

To the boy's amazement the black sheep then proceeded to unveil a whole arsenal of weapons, from hand-guns to rifles. At first the boy could only stare, stunned by this array of weaponry. Then he could not resist asking if he might have one of the smaller weapons, which he could carry easily. The black sheep was proud and delighted to find his young relative showing such an appreciation of the idea of owning a weapon. More than happy to oblige, he presented the boy with a German automatic hand-gun of a type highly prized by the gun-running fraternity. The boy could hardly believe his good fortune as he took the gun with an expression of rapture on his face.

As a result of this unforgettable incident, the giver and the receiver were to form an even closer bond. They saw each other more often and the boy's perception of their friendship changed as it became clear that the black sheep considered him his chosen one. He was now being treated as a man and no longer as a boy. Wardeh and Jamileh, however, were horrified when they heard the story of the gun. They begged the boy to return it. The gun, they insisted, was the tool of the devil. It was bound to bring bad luck in its wake. But the boy could not begin to entertain the possibility of its return. So far as he was concerned, the gun was the greatest compliment that had ever been paid to him by another man. He treasured it with such a passion that its loss would have been too painful to contemplate. Eventually the old ladies gave way and accepted defeat, though the trepidation they felt remained.

The boy slept with the gun under his pillow. He also often carried it during the day, though he was careful to keep it concealed from view. The gun had become his closest companion and he spent hours polishing and cleaning it. He would use an empty petrol can for target practice with live ammunition in the garden. The old ladies were terrified at the noise. Jamileh bore the brunt of all this firing, for he would tease her unmercifully, pretending he was about to use her earthenware jug, full of heavenly water from the Fountain of Mary, for his prime target. As he took aim she would scream for her sister and, for once, beg for the help of the Almighty to intercede on her behalf. But it had only been done in fun, and the scene always ended with Wardeh and Jamileh embracing the boy and telling him how much they loved him despite his impish behaviour.

In the days preceding the formation of the state of Israel, the civil war became more violent and bloody by the hour. Eventually Wardeh's son deemed it too dangerous to remain in the house on Mountain Road. With almost no notice, the exodus of the Palestinians from their homes began, and Wardeh's son, with his wife and three daughters, suddenly arrived in Nazareth to join the boy and the two old ladies in the little two-roomed house. In an emergency, blood becomes thicker than water. Although the old ladies still had a bitter memory of their eviction from the Mountain Road house, they welcomed the whole family of Wardeh's son to share their home. Naturally their two rooms now became extremely crowded, with not an inch of ground to spare. Wardeh and Jamileh moved into the small kitchen room with the attic store, and the family took over the whole of the larger room. Naturally, too, the boy found the development stifling, especially with his father invading, as it were, a territory he had made his own. There was an instant tension in the air that heralded trouble in the coming weeks.

The boy had come to see himself in a different light, encouraged by the attentions of the black sheep. The freedoms he had enjoyed during two years of living with his grandmother and great-aunt had made him more mature. He was no longer in awe of his father and was not going to tolerate the flare-ups of foul temper and violent reactions that had been a feature of their family life for so many years. The one hope the boy had was that his father might have become aware of the unacceptable pugnaciousness of his ways; might even be able to transform himself into the sort of benevolent father who presides over his family with love and understanding. Such possibilities were a vain dream. With the political situation looking ever more bleak, the father became more aggressive out of total frustration and vented his anger on his family, creating consternation and havoc as a result.

The peaceful, happy days he had spent living with the two old ladies were, the boy realized, a thing of the past. In their place was a positive maelstrom of domestic strife. The day came when, in a fit of rabid rage, the father struck his son and the son found it impossible not to react. He ran into the garden and picked up a large rock with which he threatened to strike his father down. There was a terrifying determination on the face of the boy that no one had ever seen before. Flushed with anger, he shook as he brandished the rock, almost beyond being responsible for his actions. Who knows what might have happened without the quick intervention of his beloved grandmother and her sister? Hurling harsh words at the father, they calmed the boy, got him to put down the piece of rock, took him into their small room and bolted the door. The stand-off lasted for three days and three nights, until the boy's father began to weep and beg forgiveness. After that all was well, at least for the duration of the family's stay in Nazareth.

With the declaration of the state of Israel (and no sign of a fulfilment of the promises made under the British Mandate), hostilities started to simmer down and Wardeh's son began to make arrangements to take his family back to the city. The parting from the two old ladies was bound to be a harrowing wrench. But the boy knew that sooner or later he must leave to pursue his studies abroad and there could be no future for him in Nazareth. He would have to move away from the shadow of his father and make a clean break. The process had come to seem as inevitable as it was painful. Wardeh and Jamileh were well into the twilight of their lives and resigned to what must happen. Their life-expectancy diminished with the passing of each day. The boy wondered if he would ever see them again, and he asked himself if this was to be the last farewell.

One evening he went to say goodbye to the black sheep and tell him about their imminent departure. The black sheep embraced him over and over again. With a rifle slung over his shoulder as well as the hand-gun he always carried under his white robe, he gave the boy safe escort back to the old ladies' house, declaring that should the boy ever encounter any enemies in his life, then he must not hesitate to let him deal with the matter as he saw fit – presumably in his own uncompromising way. The guarantee was both alarming and reassuring.

The next day preparations began for the return to the big city. The first thing the boy did was to take the gun that he had kept so close to him for the past months out of its secure place. He wrapped it in a fine linen cloth, placed it in a tin box and buried it underneath the chicken shed. He realized that this was another farewell, that he would probably never see the gun again.

When it came to bidding goodbye to the old

ladies, the boy's feelings reached a pitch of heart-rending intensity. Indeed his heart rate increased so dramatically that he almost swooned and had to fight to stay on his feet. Wardeh and Jamileh wept, and wept, and wept again. It was truly the end of an era.

Back in the big city, the family's original home had been partly destroyed and the remaining part illegally occupied. The best accommodation they could find was a flat in a British compound on the other side of Mountain Road. It was on the ground floor and had a small garden and open yard. The boy occupied the smallest room. This was his choice, to preserve his privacy. The alternative would have been to share the big bedroom with all the others. The usual tension was in the air, but the boy had become more philosophical about it. He accepted now that his father would probably never change, but he also knew that his father would never again dare to provoke him into a fight. The odds were no longer stacked in his father's favour.

In his new room, the boy often lay on his bed, thinking fondly of the two old ladies who had brought such fulfilling joy into his life. He remembered such things as Jamileh planting an olive tree in the garden. When he asked her why she did so, since it would be such a long time before it could bear fruit, she replied, 'They planted and we eat. Now we plant that they may eat.' Another time a priest called, and, seeing the beautiful flowers in the garden, wanted to pick some for his church, free of charge, like the monks on a previous occasion. Jamileh was once again emphatic in her refusal. She and her sister could ill afford to be decorating churches, she said, when they were so needy themselves. Jamileh and the clergy could never be described as being on good terms, and her attitude did not seem likely to change, even when the gates of heaven themselves came in sight.

The boy would try to imagine what the old ladies might be doing. Was Wardeh working at her needlework, complaining of the way her eyesight was beginning to fail? Was Jamileh climbing the precarious ladder to the attic to fetch down some crushed wheat (which she cooked by steaming, as it was less expensive than rice). Were the hens earning their keep by maintaining a good supply of eggs to gladden Jamileh's heart each morning? Peasant life was full of uncertainty. It relied on elements over which man had no control – the vagaries of nature.

Six months later the boy left the country and went abroad to pursue his higher education. The scheme did not go as planned, however. His father retired at the age of fifty-three and no longer had the resources to fund his son's scholastic endeavours. The boy had to abandon his education and find work to support himself. Two more years went by. One day a priest arrived from the Holy Land, bringing with him a few golden sovereigns entrusted to him by the boy's father. At last the boy was able to take a boat home for a brief visit to his family. On board he befriended two Jewish girls who were sisters, on their way to Israel to work on a kibbutz. The three of them got on extremely well during the five-day voyage and made a pact that they would meet up again during the week after landing. This, in fact, they did.

The boy was warmly greeted by his parents and for once was glad to find himself at home. His father's personality was unchanged. His temper remained as unpredictable as ever, though physically he was less strong than he had been. He gave the impression of having aged beyond his years and his walk was unsteady, especially when going uphill. The boy's three sisters had grown up, and the eldest was married to a clever carpenter. His mother was, as ever, subservient to her husband and was never allowed to have any real identity of her own. She had always been very protective of her son, but when it came to the crunch in the family rows had been able to do very little. There was no doubting that she loved her son devotedly, as he loved her, but she would never become a major influence in his life.

During his stay at home he often went out to meet the Jewish sisters he had befriended on the boat. He became romantically linked with the younger one, and they spent most evenings in a park overlooking the bay, engaging in the sort of love-making activities that in those days left its mark on the clothes of young males. His mother would be horrified next day to find the stains on his trousers, and would hastily wash them out of sight of her daughters. Finally the boy invited the two Jewish sisters to go with him on a visit to Nazareth so he could see his grandmother and great-aunt again, after an absence of two years. It was intensely moving for the boy to see the old ladies again and to spend one last night in their company in the house. As he and the two girls lay on mattresses on the floor, he heard again the convent bell being rung at intervals as the nuns continued to glorify the Lord throughout the night.

The ringing of that bell evoked a stream of memories from his childhood of the time in the big city when he used to attend school with his sisters at a convent, where they were taught by nuns. Those nuns were of a different religious order from the ones in Nazareth. They were open to the world in their mission and glorified God through their teaching. They were kind and considerate, and some of them were beautiful. Their skin had a honeydew texture and their rosy cheeks glistened in bright daylight. In his total innocence, in an atmosphere intensified by the beauty of the services and redolent with incense, the boy had experienced the first ripples of sexual desire. Later he was able to explain these as the stirrings of a healthy lust, but then his young body had shivered at the thought of an embrace or a hug from one of the nuns. He grew up imagining that the worldly abstinence of the beautiful nuns made their bodies, heavily shrouded in their dark habits, throw off such powerful sexual vibrations that they must be utterly devastating and represented the very epitome of the forbidden fruit.

Soon he would have to go abroad again. He had no idea when his next return to the Holy Land would be. In his heart he knew that this must be the last time he would see the old ladies. They were managing to continue with a daily routine, but it was clear they were entering the closing stages of their lives.

When the boy had left their care to return to the big city with his family, they had missed the mutual nurturing and daily interaction of the different generations. All of that had been like nothing they had ever experienced before. Once the boy was no longer with them, they had been overcome by a sense of loneliness, feeling they were aimlessly going through the motions of life until the time came for them to be judged. Whereas Wardeh was inclined to believe in life after death, Jamileh was more sceptical. They would debate the issue, though they never resolved it. Wardeh prayed aloud while Jamileh mumbled to herself incoherently. What the mumbling signified was never clear. It was a secret Jamileh would take with her to the grave.

Wardeh was spending most of her spare time absorbed in the needlework she had learned as a child. Their family was renowned for its skill in producing tablecloths that grew to be highly prized by specialized collectors of that type of traditional embroidered art. It was an intricate and delicate craft that involved much patience, a good eye and a capacity for sustained concentration. Wardeh's illiteracy was no barrier to her artistic flair in creating pieces much admired for their craftsmanship and beauty. These would command a high price on the tourist market and rich merchants often sought to buy them as dowries for their daughters. Wardeh sold each piece as soon as she finished it, and with the money she would buy gold coins that were relics of the Ottoman Empire, still considered a highly desirable currency, and bury them in the tin box under the chicken shed. This practice of burying any treasure they had in their favourite hiding place was something the old ladies followed diligently. It was a safeguard against the possibility of theft, even though such things rarely happened in that part of the world, at least in those days.

But old age brings with it some haunting insecurities. Wardeh was aware that her eyes were failing her. The loss of sharpness in her sight meant, as the years went past, that she was able to do less and less of the more intricate work. She became inclined to retain her more elaborate pieces in a small collection with a view to passing them on to her granddaughters as dowries when the time came for them to marry.

Jamileh, on the other hand, was not endowed with the sort of gifts that her sister possessed. Her talents were entirely focused on the practicalities of harvesting her crops and growing exquisite flowers. Her garden produce she could barter for butter or other dairy items that they needed. She was nothing if not streetwise and the neighbourhood perceived her as a hard nut to crack. In general she was good-natured, though she seldom laughed, and the slightest criticism, whatever its source, made her take instant umbrage. Where Wardeh saw the world in a benign light, Jamileh viewed it with a degree of cynicism and trusted no one. She expected no favours and would not have accepted any were they to be offered. Her independence of spirit manifested itself in every aspect of her life; it was a code of living to which she remained true to the end.

The boy, now grown to manhood, returned to the West, and the West became his home. The heritage his grandmother and great-aunt had given him proved to be his most valued asset. His memory of their example was for him a constant affirmation of the redemption of the soul and the ability of the human spirit to overcome through struggle and tenacity. The abrasiveness of his father, though it led to harshness and distress at the time, was not long-lasting as an influence. Wardeh's grandson had learnt by reaction to be unafraid to experiment, to show a pioneering spirit in his daily life that went against the conventions of security. He could speculate and lose and learn the lesson of the loss, never expecting rewards that were undeserved. The struggle to be nothing like his father had opened his eyes to the traps life could lay in one's path and he bore his father no grudge. The loss of his childhood had been regrettable, but it had no adverse effect on his subsequent life. A love of the arts remained the one positive legacy from his father that endured.

The son often reflected on his relationship with his father. He appreciated the loneliness and the sense of not belonging that must have dominated a major part of his father's life. Above all, there had been the time Wardeh's son spent in the German orphanage. He never complained of receiving harsh treatment there, but it seemed certain he must have missed being given any parental love at first hand, due to the fact that his mother could not be near him and he never knew his father. Nevertheless, there were times when Wardeh's son showed a deeply loving concern for his own son. He became almost hysterical with worry whenever he feared the boy's health was in jeopardy. Instinctively he would put his arms round the boy's frail body and hug him, tears running down his cheeks. There were other displays of equal intensity, but they rarely lasted for long.

The demons that haunted Wardeh's son really never left him. They would surface at the least provocation or whenever events took an unwelcome turn. Then he would lose his usual composure and resort to violent outbursts that were both ugly and undignified. The most exasperating aspect of this trait in his personality was the way he was able to conceal it from the outside world, to which he invariably managed to present himself as the most stable and loving of parents, doting on his children. In the public perception there was never a trace of the destructive flaw in his character that was to alienate him from his own son for so many years.

For the boy, it was the love he experienced in the care of the two old ladies that allowed him eventually to love his father, and to bow to that perversity that earned the status of fatherhood respect in those parts of the world whatever the quality of the fathering. Perhaps it was also because time is the great healer, as the old ladies affirmed, and the dramatic impact that events have had in the past somehow give way to more measured assessments.

It could never be said that Wardeh's son mellowed, even in his old age, but he was immensely proud of the boy and his early achievements. There was a bundle of poems and short stories written in Arabic by the boy at the age of nine that his father kept tucked away in a safe drawer in his favourite mahogany cabinet. They were discovered there after his death.

The boy's instinct that he felt he was seeing the old ladies for the last time proved to be correct. Not long afterwards they became too old and infirm to carry on living in their little house in Nazareth. Wardeh's son then moved his mother to the big city, where she occupied the little bedroom that had been the boy's. There she died of suspected tuberculosis at the age of eighty-five. Jamileh was put into a hospice for the aged run by nuns. She passed peacefully away in her sleep at eighty-seven.

After the deaths of the old ladies, Wardeh's son lost no time in selling the house in Nazareth. He let it go for a paltry sum. The house was of no interest to him, sentimental or otherwise, and he did not want the responsibility of maintaining it.

Wardeh's grandson was broken-hearted when he heard the news. He could not believe that his father had disposed so casually of the property which meant so much to him personally. In the grandson's mind the little house was a shrine to the memory of his grandmother and her sister, who had guided and nurtured him through a very difficult phase of his life. He owed so much to them, not least the gift of what remained of his youth and the chance to win his freedom.

Already he had been cherishing a dream that one day, when the time came for old age to claim him, he would make a pilgrimage to the house in Nazareth and spend a night sleeping alone on a mattress in the big room. For one last night, he had thought, he would lie and listen to the sound of the blessed nuns' convent bell ringing out through the darkness. Fulfilling the dream would have been a culmination, though just to dream it was still a worthy tribute to the old ladies. He continued to believe that they kept a watchful eye on him from beyond the grave.

How could I have come to know this moving tale of a family, who, like many others, fought dissension and heartache, with all its details of pathos, unless I had lived amongst them? The truth is that Wardeh was my grandmother and her son was my father. Jamileh, her sister, was my great-aunt, and the boy was me.